Terminal Madness

by Judd Winick

A Division of Macmillan Computer Publishing
201 W. 103rd St., Indianapolis, IN 46290 USA

Library of Congress Catalog Card Number: 96-070545

International Standard Book Number: 0-7897-0971-6

98 97 96   8 7 6 5 4 3 2 1

Interpretation of the printing code: the rightmost double-digit number is the year of the book's first printing; the rightmost single-digit number is the number of the book's printing. For example, a printing code of 96-1 shows that this copy of the book was printed during the first printing of the book in 1996.

Printed in the United States of America

Publisher   Roland Elgey

Publishing Manager   Lynn E. Zingraf

Editorial Services Director   Elizabeth Keaffaber

Managing Editor   Michael Cunningham

Acquisitions Editor   Martha O'Sullivan

Production Editor   Katie Purdum

Book Designer   Dan Armstrong

Cover Designer   Judd Winick

Production Team   Marcia Brizendine, DiMonique Ford, Kay Hoskin, Beth Lewis, Sossity Smith

Photo By   Ken Probst

Zippy Tone Boy   Barry Pruett

HE WAS TRYING TO ORDER PIZZA, BUT ENTERED INTO THE WRONG PROGRAM AND GAVE ALL OUR MONEY TO THE REPUBLICAN PARTY...
WE'RE GONNA TRY TO MOVE YOU NOW, MR. RICHARDS!
GOOD LUCK ON GETTING **THAT** BACK.
EMS
EMS
WINICK©

BRAD'S LIFE TOOK ON NEW MEANING WHEN HE DISCOVERED THAT HIS SOUND CARD COULD MAKE REALLY DISGUSTING NOISES.

IT WAS WHEN BEN SWITCHED FROM **MAC** TO **IBM** THAT THE NIGHTMARES STARTED.

MULTIMEDIA SOFTWARE EMBARRASSMENT

JIM GETS TOO PERSONAL WITH HIS **PC**

HOW JACOB AND BESSIE'S STRANGE, BUT TENDER ROMANCE BEGAN.

WE GOT A MODEM, A CD ROM DRIVE, A SOUND CARD, A LASER PRINTER, A SECOND HARD DRIVE, WE'RE HOOKED UP TO THE INTERNET, A FLOPPY DISK DRIVE, A SCANNER, FOUR INTEGRATED SOFTWARE PACKAGES, AN ADJUSTABLE KEYBOARD, AND SOME THIRTY GAME PROGRAMS. WE JUST DON'T OWN A COMPUTER...
BLEW BILLY'S COLLEGE FUND.
Mel
CD ROM
VICTIMS OF BRAD MELTZER- THE MOST RUTHLESS COMPUTER SALESMAN IN NORTH AMERICA.
WINICK©

THE TEDIUM OF WEB SITES IN THE ANIMAL KINGDOM...

ON MONDAY, THE FIFTH FLOOR OFFICE WAS GETTING A FULL SYSTEMS UPGRADE. ON FRIDAY, THEY "TOOK CARE OF" THE OLD SYSTEMS...

IT BEGAN WITH JUST GOING ON AMERICA ONLINE, I WAS IN SOME OF THE CHAT ROOMS... THEN THERE WERE MORE CHAT ROOMS AND MORE CHAT ROOMS, (SOB) THEN BEFORE I REALIZED IT, I WAS ONLINE ALL THE TIME TALKING TO ANYONE WHO WOULD LISTEN. I WAS POSTING ON THE "HAMSTER CARE BILLBOARD", I DON'T EVEN OWN A HAMSTER!!
EASY...
WE'VE ALL BEEN THERE...
TWELVE STEP INTERNET PROGRAM
WINICK©

OGG WAS AHEAD OF HIS TIME...

WHEN BROWSERS GET TIRED OF THE WEB...

TERRY AND DIANE DON'T HAVE TO DRESS UP LIKE
AMAZONS WHEN THEY FIGURE OUT A NEW APPLICATION...
BUT THEY **LIKE** IT...

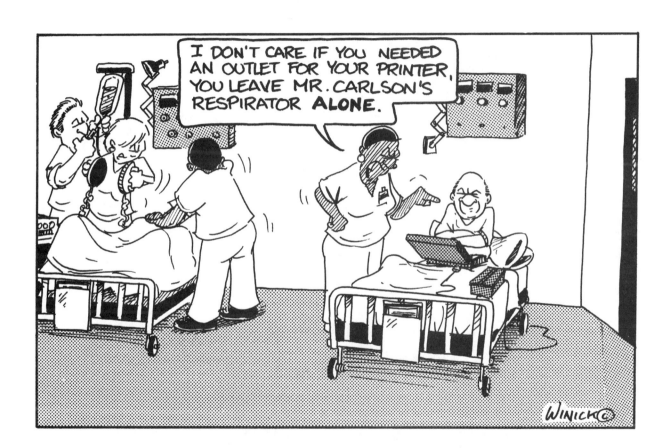

TED DIDN'T KNOW WHAT THE CHICKENS WERE DOING ON HIS COMPUTER... BUT HE KNEW IT COULDN'T BE GOOD.

HONESTY ON THE INTERNET

MELVIN SHEKTNER, THE MOST FORGOTTEN CHARACTER FROM THE WIZARD OF OZ.

AT THE SAME DISGUSTING MOMENT JERRY AND HIS MOTHER REALIZED THEY WERE IN THE PRIVATE CHAT ROOM OF THE SWINGING SINGLES SITE... **TOGETHER.**

MOMENTS IN COMPUTER HELL
MISSING THE SAVE

SIGNS THAT A BUSINESS DEAL ISN'T GOING TOO WELL...

LOUISIANA CD ROM FIGHT

EMERGENCY COMPUTER GEEKS

COMPUTER NAPPING.

GREAT MOMENTS IN COMPUTER HISTORY...

WE'VE GOT WEBSITES!!

OUTDOING HIS "E-MAIL OFF THE COFFEE MAKER" TRIUMPH OF '93, JIMMY "SWISS-ARMY" VANDERBILT, LOGS ONTO THE INTERNET VIA THE MICROWAVE.

FROM THE LOOK OF THE SCREENSAVERS MR. MURPHY COULD TELL THAT HIS POPULARITY WITH HIS EMPLOYEES HAD DIPPED JUST A BIT...

ALAN HAD SOME TROUBLE WITH THE NEW GAME...

MODEM PROBLEMS

AN AVID RECYCLER AND A CRUEL EMPLOYER, MR. POMERANTZ ALWAYS LOVED KILLING TWO BIRDS WITH ONE STONE...

LET YOUR INNER GOALS BE COMPLETED THROUGH THOUGHT AS WELL AS ACTIONS. SEEK UNDERSTANDING THROUGH REASON AND PAITIENCE, AND I THINK YOUR PRINTER IS HAVING A FEEDER PROBLEM...
THANKS...
NO SWEAT...
WINICK©

NELSON LIKED TO RENDER FAMILY MEMBERS BUT REPLACE THEIR HEADS WITH EGGPLANTS... HE'S SEEKING THERAPY.

WINICK ©

EDITING ... THE EARLY DAYS

SKIP HAD SOME TROUBLE WITH THE NEW MODEM...

IN A BIZARRE TURN OF EVENTS, COUNT DRACULA IS DESTROYED BY A SUN ICON ON HIS NEW GRAPHICAL USER INTERFACE.

BARRY LOSES HIS "TONGUE IN THE DISK DRIVE" BET ... AGAIN.

COMPUTER GEEKS AND ODDITIES

JANINE VAN DORF, WORLD'S FASTEST TYPIST.

VINCE "DISC DRIVE" BERNBAUM

WINICK ©

JIMMY THE LIVING PRINTER BOY

MARK "MODEM" WILSON

THE PLEASURE OF A HOME OFFICE

JIM'S TURN TO FIX THE PRINTER.